sip

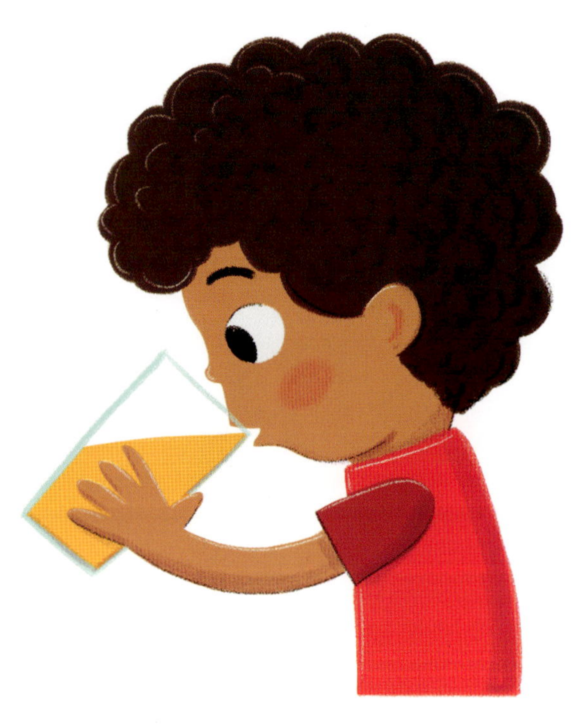

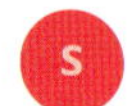
s
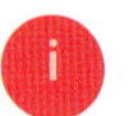
i
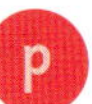
p

sit

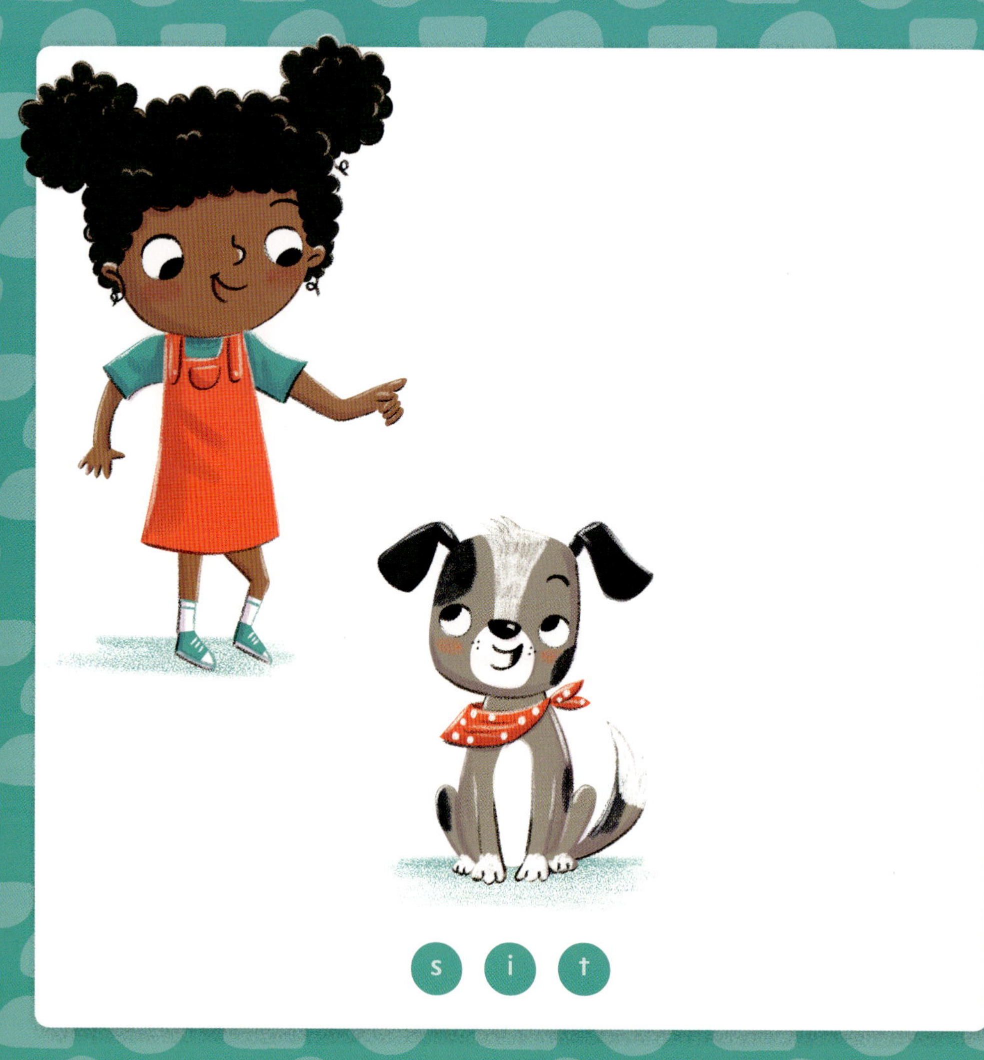
s i t

tin

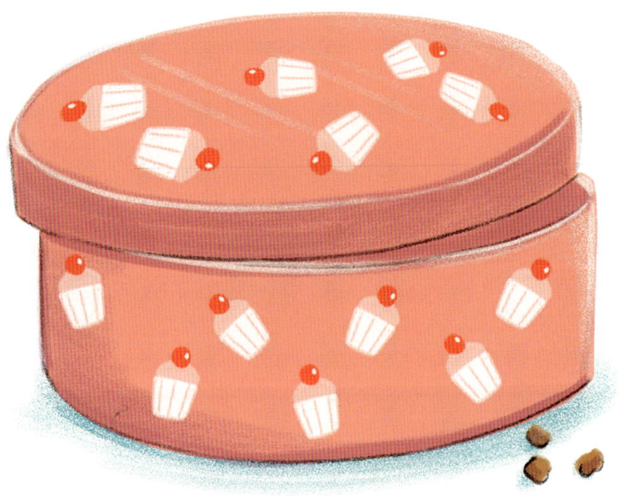

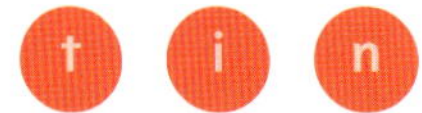
t i n

pan

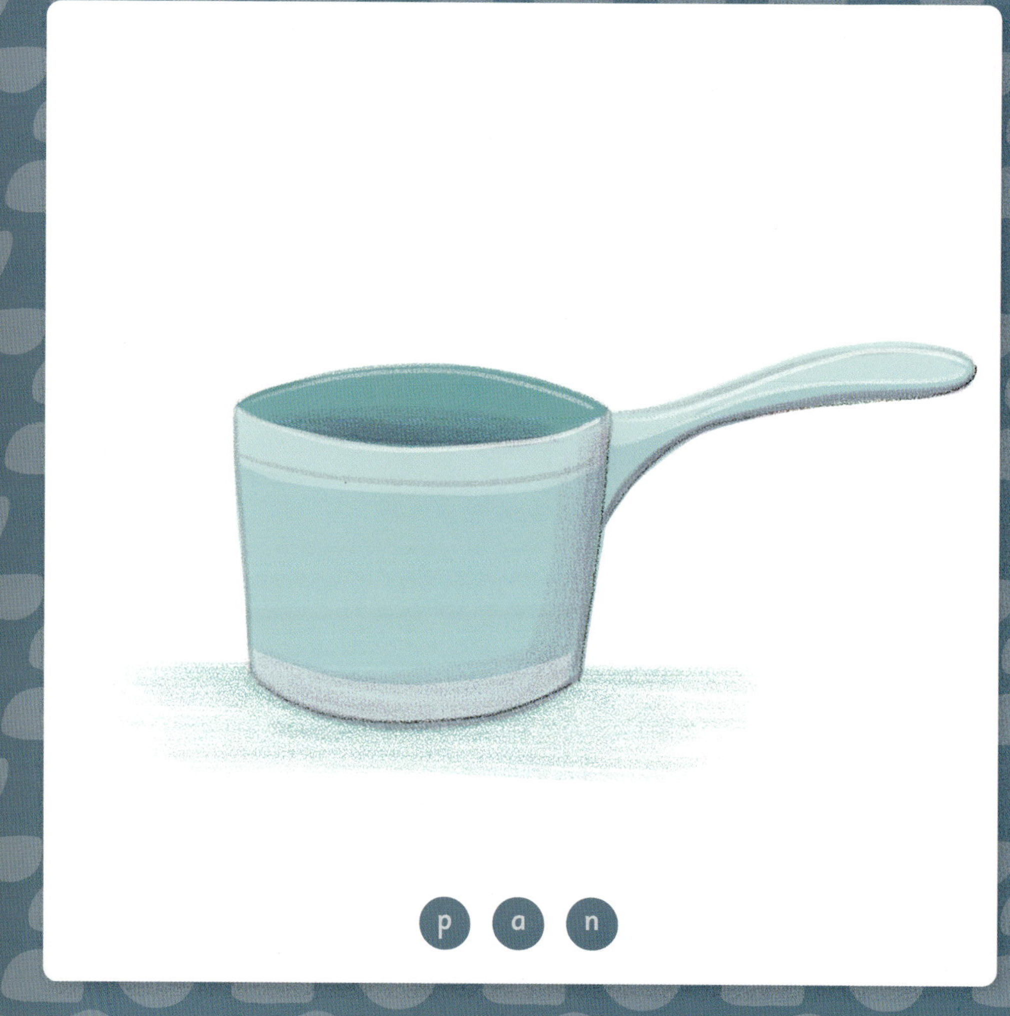
p a n

pin

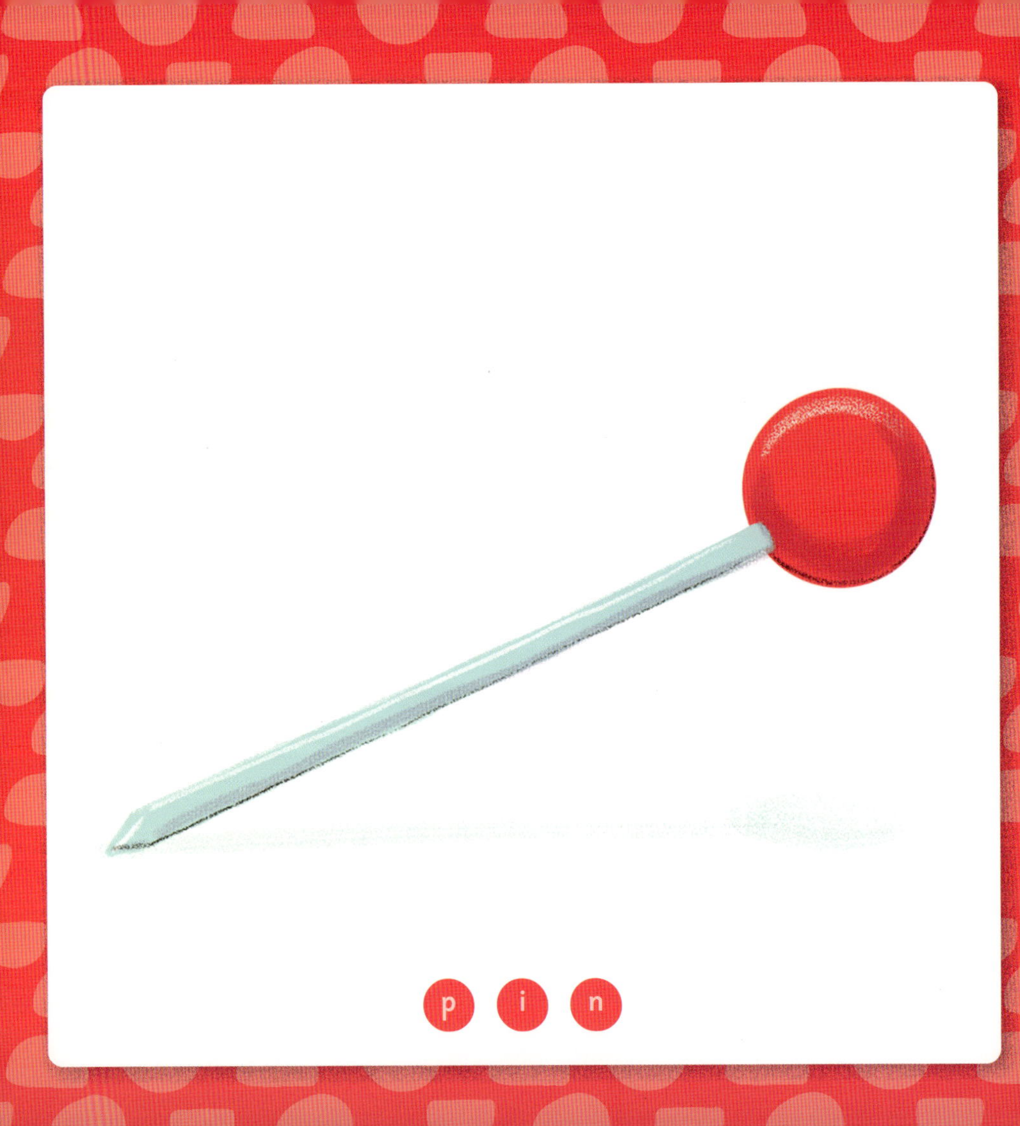
p i n

nap

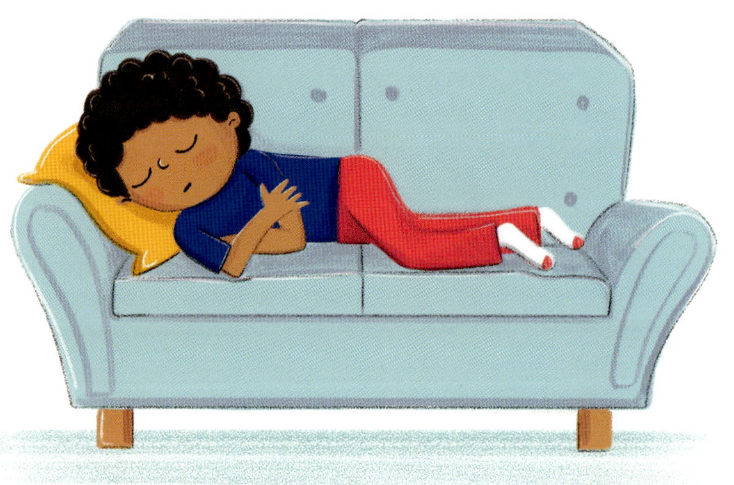

n
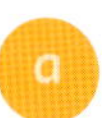
a

p

snip

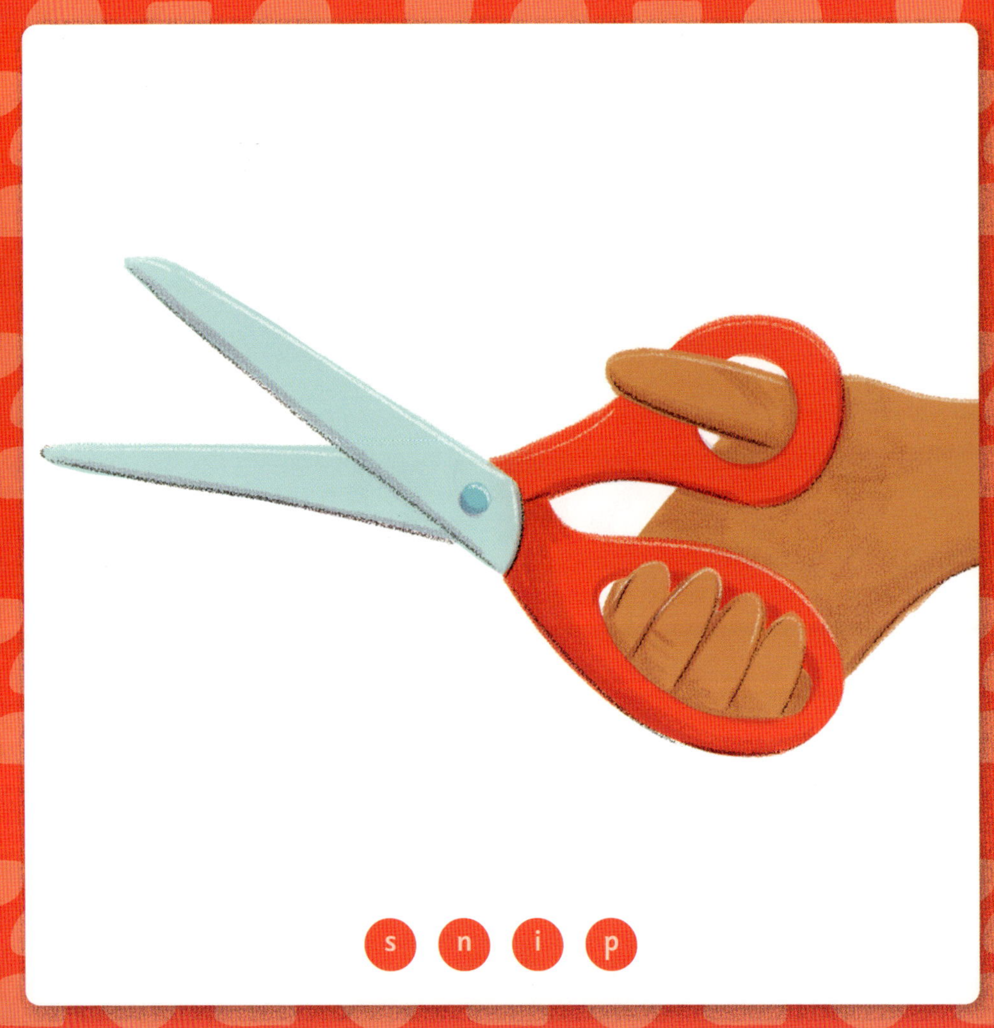
s n i p

spin

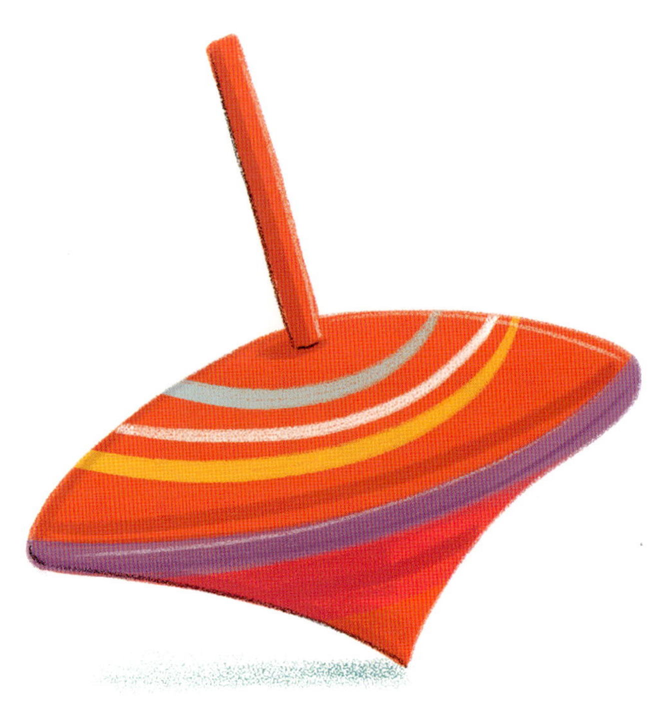

s p i n